Dalia Says Goodbye to Grandpa

by **Sarah, Duchess of York**

Illustrated by Ian Cunliffe

Dalia Says Goodbye to Grandpa

helping hand books

First published in Great Britain 2007 by Lloyds Pharmacy Ltd
Sapphire Court, Walsgrave Triangle, Coventry CV2 2TX
www.lloydspharmacy.com

In consultation with Cameron Wilson Ltd

Illustrated by Ian Cunliffe

'Ten Helpful Hints' contributed by Dr. Richard Woolfson,
child psychologist, Fellow of the British Psychological Society.

Printed in China

British Library Cataloguing in Publication Data
A catalogue record for this book is available from the British Library

ISBN 978-1-906260-07-1

All children face many new experiences as they grow up and helping
them to understand and deal with each is one of the most demanding
and rewarding things we do as parents. The helping hand books are
for both children and parents to read, perhaps together. Each simple
story describes a childhood experience and shows some of the ways
in which to make it a positive one. I do hope these books encourage
children and parents to talk about these sometimes difficult issues;
talking together goes a long way to finding a solution.

Sarah

Sarah, Duchess of York

Dalia loved her Grandpa very much. He had grey hair and a beard and was always smiling and laughing. When Dalia was little, he made up stories about a magical land and when she was older, he would tell her jokes. Sometimes they were not very good jokes but Grandpa used to laugh so much that Dalia just had to join in.

Recently Grandpa had not ben very well and had to go into hospital.

Dalia and her Mum had gone to see him. Before they went into the ward, Mum had said,

"Grandpa may not be feeling so good so we need to cheer him up."

Dalia had been sad to see her Grandpa in hospital. He looked weak and seemed much smaller than before.

Dalia remembered what her Mum had said and told Grandpa what she had been doing at school and about a trip they had been on recently to a farm.

"You should have seen it, Grandpa," said Dalia,

"there were huge cows, much bigger than I thought they would be, and sheep with really curly woolly coats!

And there were lovely goats. We were allowed to stroke them. And they had beards," she laughed,
"just like yours!"

"I know, I'll draw you a picture of a goat! Would you like that Grandpa?"
Grandpa smiled one of his warm smiles that Dalia loved so much.

Some days later her Mum and Dad came into her room just as she was waking up. They both looked very sad and she could see that her Mum had been crying. Her Dad sat on the side of her bed and took her hand,

"I am afraid I have some very sad news." he said, "Grandpa passed away in his sleep last night."

At first, Dalia found it hard to understand what her Dad was saying.

"But I'm going to see him next week. I've almost finished drawing the goat and I want him to see it. He must see it." she cried.

"He would have loved to see it," said her Mum gently, "and I know he would want you to finish it anyhow."

Dalia and her Mum and Dad shared a huge hug.

During the next few days Dalia kept thinking about her Grandpa and imagining that he would soon be back, sitting in his favourite chair, laughing and joking with her.

It was too hard to think that she would never see him again.

Dalia saw how upset her Mum was and felt she should not cry or talk about Grandpa in case it upset her Mum more.

One night, she was reading in bed and her Dad came to see her.

"Grandpa was very proud of you, you know," he said and Dalia just burst into tears.

"I'm so sad," she sobbed, "I don't think I'll ever be happy again."

"Think of it like this," said her Dad, "the sun will shine again but not today."

"But who will be the next to die?"
asked Dalia tearfully.

"Well, it comes to us all,"
said her Dad,
"but if we all spent our
time worrying about it,
that wouldn't be very
sensible would it?

The important thing is to
live our lives to the full and
treat each day as special.
Your Grandpa certainly
did that.

And he will always be
with us in our memories."

The next day, when Dalia was getting ready for school her Dad had asked if she wanted to stay at home for the day but she decided she would rather be with her school friends, getting on with school life than sitting at home thinking about Grandpa.

Her friends knew that she was sad and tried to cheer her up; even her best friend Juma gave her a hug which wasn't really like him at all and almost made her burst into tears again!

The form teacher, Mrs Collins
settled everyone down and said,

"Now, as we all know, Dalia has had a very
sad time with the loss of her grandfather.

Why don't we spend a few minutes thinking
about someone special to each of us; a
grandparent, an aunt or uncle, something
memorable about them that you can
tell us about?"

14

Everyone in the class had something different to say. Some 'memorable moments' were so funny that Dalia couldn't help but giggle; the aunt who never took her hat off, the grandad who 'cooked' lunch without the oven on and the uncle who sent postcards from all over the world without stamps!

When Dalia got home from school, she saw that Mum had covered the table with photographs of Grandpa; some when he was a young man and some when he was Grandpa.

After tea, Dalia and her Mum and Dad all began to tell stories about Grandpa, about the many happy times they had all had together.

That night, as Dalia lay in her bed, she felt so much better.

Her Grandpa had been so special and she knew she would miss him a lot.

"He may not be here in this house any longer," she thought, "but Grandpa will always have a place in my heart. And I shall finish that drawing of a goat for him tomorrow."

TEN HELPFUL HINTS
TO HELP CHILDREN COPE WITH BEREAVEMENT

by Dr. Richard Woolfson

1. Encourage your child to use words to express what he is thinking and feeling about the bereavement – let him know that it is perfectly alright to show emotions.

2. Try to be calm. One of the major difficulties you face when discussing bereavement with your child is that you are grieving too. If you become distressed during the discussion he'll become confused and afraid.

3. Listen carefully. Your child's feelings about grief are very real, and they can be very intense. He may not be an adult but he feels emotional pain all the same.

4. Give support. A warm cuddle from you may just be what he needs to help him through this difficult time; a loving gesture like that can ease his distress, and can be more powerful than a long, serious discussion.

5. Make opportunities for creative play. Some children are able to release their inner feelings through creative or imaginative play, perhaps by drawing or making something.

6. Your child might like to talk about the person who has died, perhaps bringing out photographs and other reminders. This can be a useful part of the healing process, even when it takes place close to the bereavement.

7. Give lots of reassurance. The death of a friend or relative can make a child frightened and insecure because he worries that others may die too. He constantly seeks reassurance that everybody close to him is safe and well.

8. Give your child time. His pace of recovery from the loss of a loved one may take much longer than you would like or expect. Allow him time to adjust to a world without that person, however long that takes.

9. Explain death using your own words. Some parents tell their child that the dead grandparent has gone to heaven and is amongst the angels. Others says that death is like going to sleep and never waking up.

10. Keep a close watch on him in the days and weeks following the bereavement and look for any changes in his behaviour that might indicate that he is stressed. Don't assume that he copes well with bereavement just because he smiles a lot.

The helping hand books

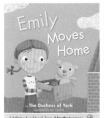

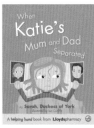

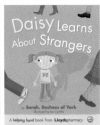

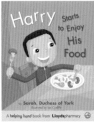

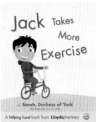

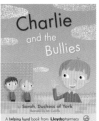

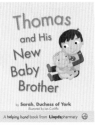

Lloydspharmacy